外公的神秘藏宝

【美】露西·瑞切·潘纳◎著
【美】杰瑞·史麦斯◎绘
范晓星◎译

天津出版传媒集团

新蕾出版社

图书在版编目（CIP）数据

外公的神秘藏宝/（美）潘纳（Penner,L.R.）著；（美）史麦斯（Smath,J.）绘；范晓星译.
—天津:新蕾出版社,2015.5(2024.12重印)
(数学帮帮忙·互动版)
书名原文:X Marks the Spot!
ISBN 978-7-5307-6216-5

Ⅰ.①外…
Ⅱ.①潘…②史…③范…
Ⅲ.①数学–儿童读物
Ⅳ.①01–49

中国版本图书馆 CIP 数据核字(2015)第 058646 号

X Marks the Spot! by Lucille Recht Penner;
Illustrated by Jerry Smath.
Copyright ⓒ 2002 by Kane Press, Inc.
All rights reserved, including the right of reproduction in whole or in part in any form. This edition published by arrangement with Kane Press, Inc. New York, NY, represented by Lerner Publishing Group through The ChoiceMaker Korea Co. agency.
Simplified Chinese translation copyright ⓒ 2015 by New Buds Publishing House (Tianjin) Limited Company
ALL RIGHTS RESERVED
本书中文简体版专有出版权经由中华版权代理中心授予新蕾出版社(天津)有限公司。未经许可,不得以任何方式复制或抄袭本书的任何部分。
津图登字:02–2012–239

出版发行 天津出版传媒集团
新蕾出版社
http://www.newbuds.com.cn

地　　址:天津市和平区西康路 35 号(300051)
出 版 人:马玉秀
电　　话:总编办 (022)23332422
　　　　　发行部 (022)23332679　23332351
传　　真:(022)23332422
经　　销:全国新华书店
印　　刷:天津新华印务有限公司
开　　本:787mm×1092mm　1/16
印　　张:3
版　　次:2015 年 5 月第 1 版　2024 年 12 月第 22 次印刷
定　　价:12.00 元

无处不在的数学

资深编辑　卢　江

　　人们常说"兴趣是最好的老师",有了兴趣,学习就会变得轻松愉快。数学对于孩子来说或许有些难,因为比起语文,数学显得枯燥、抽象,不容易理解,孩子往往不那么喜欢。可许多家长都知道,学数学对于孩子的成长和今后的生活有多么重要。不仅数学知识很有用,学习数学过程中获得的数学思想和方法更会影响孩子的一生,因为数学素养是构成人基本素质的一个重要因素。但是,怎样才能让孩子对数学产生兴趣呢?怎样才能激发他们兴致勃勃地去探索数学问题呢?我认为,让孩子读些有趣的书或许是不错的选择。读了这套"数学帮帮忙",我立刻产生了想把它们推荐给教师和家长朋友们的愿望,因为这真是一套会让孩子爱上数学的好书!

　　这套有趣的图书从美国引进,原出版者是美国资深教育专家。每本书讲述一个孩子们生活中的故事,由故事中出现的问题自然地引入一个数学知识,然后通过运用数学知识解决问题。比如,从帮助外婆整理散落的纽扣引出分类,从为小狗记录藏骨头的地点引出空间方位等等。故事素材全部来源于孩子们的真实生活，不是童话，不是幻想，而是鲜活的生活实例。正是这些发生在孩子身边的故事，让孩子们懂得，数学无处不在并且非常有用；这些鲜活的实例也使得抽象的概念更易于理解，更容易激发孩子学习数学的兴趣，让他们逐渐爱上数学。这样的教育思想和方法与我国近年来提倡的数学教育理念是十分吻合的！

这是一套适合5~8岁孩子阅读的书，书中的有趣情节和生动的插画可以将抽象的数学问题直观化、形象化，为孩子的思维活动提供具体形象的支持。如果亲子共读的话，家长可以带领孩子推测情节的发展，探讨解决难题的办法，让孩子在愉悦的氛围中学到知识和方法。

值得教师和家长朋友们注意的是，在每本书的后面，出版者还加入了"互动课堂"及"互动练习"，一方面通过一些精心设计的活动让孩子巩固新学到的数学知识，进一步体会知识的含义和实际应用；另一方面帮助家长指导孩子阅读，体会故事中数学之外的道理，逐步提升孩子的阅读理解能力。

我相信孩子读过这套书后一定会明白，原来，数学不是烦恼，不是包袱，数学真能帮大忙！

为什么人们非要搬家呢？我们刚刚搬
了新家，我一点儿都不喜欢！我弟弟利奥也
不喜欢。可是妈妈却觉得很棒。

3

"为什么我们非得搬到这么古老无聊的小镇？为什么我们非得住在这座又老旧又无聊的房子里？"我抱怨道。

"杰克，"妈妈对我说，"这房子是你外公的。他在搬去佛罗里达州之前，在这里住了快一辈子。这不让人兴奋吗？"

"是让人兴奋。"我说道，但我只不过是为了让妈妈高兴。

　　利奥和我在门口玩儿。一群海鸥掠过我们的头顶。"啊！"利奥高兴地大喊。多不起眼儿的事情都能让他兴奋。

　　来信啦！我们收到了外公的明信片。我大声地读了起来：

　　嗨！杰克和利奥！我希望你们喜欢这个新家。这栋房子里面可满是惊喜哟！到阁楼里去找找吧。

　　　　　　　　　　　　　　　爱你们的外公

我俩跑上阁楼，环顾四周。这里到处是杂七杂八的旧东西：一个猫头鹰标本、几只大木箱、某人的一尊雕像。我觉得没什么意思。

这时，我看见窗台上有个闪亮的橘黄色文件夹，上面写着：藏宝图。

"有宝藏！"我说道。我一把抓起文件夹，一封信从里面掉落出来。

"杰克,你听!"利奥说,"先仔细看图,再开始寻宝!"
我打开文件夹,里面有三张地图和寻宝指南:
·从零点开始
·先向右直行
·再向上直行
·寻找线索

藏宝图 1

提示：许个愿望吧！

"寻宝游戏！"利奥喊道。

"我们开始吧！"我对他说。

我们仔细看第一张藏宝图。

"这图怎么看呀？"利奥不解地问。他把图都拿反了，赶紧正过来。

"看到图的左下角了吗？"我说道，"画的是这座房子。我们从这里开始。我打赌，那个大红叉就是藏宝贝的地方！"

我和弟弟来到街上。我又盯着第一张地图看。

　　"杰克，我们现在干什么？"利奥问我。

　　"我马上就告诉你。"我说，"别着急！"

　　其实，这张地图根本不是那么容易就能看明白。

　　忽然，我灵光一闪。"原来这张图上的条条线
线，就是这些街道呀！"我对利奥说，"我们家的房子
就在海鸥大道和榆树街交叉的地方。"

　　"我懂了，"利奥说，"那咱们家就是这个原点
喽。"

　　我们往右边数了2条线，又往上数了3条线，正
好是大红叉的地方。

　　"说明我们要走5个街口。"我说道，"不算远！"

　　妈妈来到门口，我问她我们可不可以出去逛逛，但我没告诉她宝藏的事，我想给她一个惊喜。

　　"这个小镇看起来还不错嘛！"我说。妈妈用奇怪的表情看着我。

　　"真高兴你们开始喜欢这里了。"她说，"晚饭前回来哟。"

利奥和我沿着海鸥大道往前走。我们数着经过的每条街。第 1 条街：柳树街，第 2 条街：枫树街。

　　"那只狗狗喜欢我。"利奥说。

　　"我们一会儿还回来呢。"我说，"现在我们得走到枫树街。"

　　我们转到枫树街上，经过了天鹅街，然后是雄鹰街。

　　"鹦鹉街上有一口许愿井。"我说，"那一定就是大红叉所代表的地方！"

“这地方还不错，可这不是宝藏啊。”利奥说。

“对，它不是。”我说，“但我们可以许个愿，祝我们找到宝藏。”

我们闭上眼睛，郑重其事地许下愿望。

“如果压根儿就没有宝藏呢？”利奥问，“外公总是喜欢开玩笑。”

“他不会拿这个开玩笑的。”我对弟弟说。

许愿井

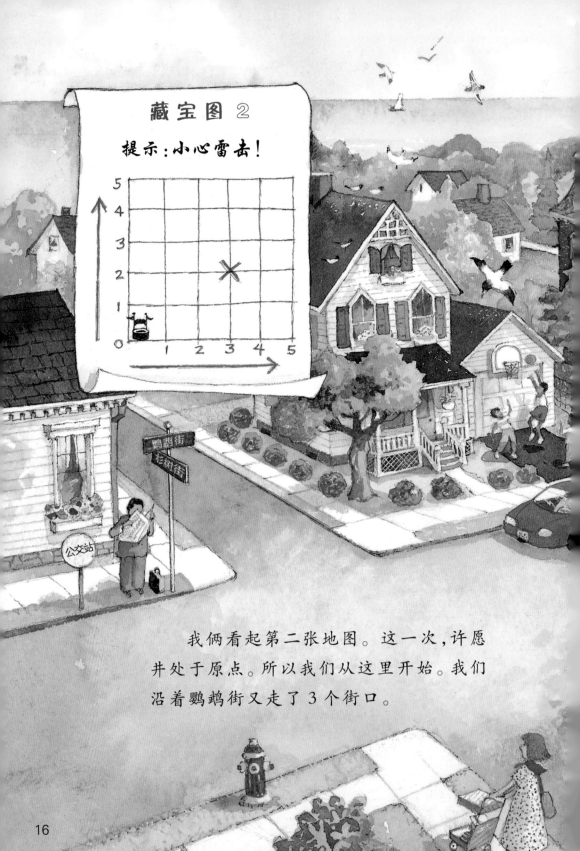

藏宝图 2

提示：小心雷击！

我俩看起第二张地图。这一次，许愿井处于原点。所以我们从这里开始。我们沿着鹦鹉街又走了 3 个街口。

　　几个男孩子在玩投篮。他们朝我们招招手。我可能终究会喜欢上这里。

　　我们拐到橡树街上，还剩 2 个街口就到了。利奥走得慢腾腾的，我对他说："宝藏可能是钻石哟！"他马上加快了步伐。

17

我们走过孔雀街，来到雪鸫街。我们俩都使劲仰头看，在街角的地方有一棵橡树，这是我见过的最大的树了。枝叶参天，最上面的树枝都是黑色的。

雪鸫街，橡树街
老橡树
种于1889年
曾于1937年和1991年
两次遭到雷击

"这棵树有点儿吓人。"利奥小声说,"咱们还是回家吧。"

"你开玩笑吗?"我喊道,"找不到宝藏,咱们就不能回家。"

利奥说:"我打赌,肯定没有宝藏。"可他还是跟我一起又看了第三张藏宝图。

　　这次,橡树街处于原点。我用手遮住地图。
"你别看。"我对利奥说,"我给你个提示:'横4
竖1。'"

　　"横4竖1?"利奥说,"太简单了!我们横着
走4条街,然后往上走1条街就到了。"

　　"正确!"我答道。

我们沿着雪鸦街走了 4 个路口。然后向上，走了 1 个路口到达白桦街。街角有一家糖果店！

"糖果！"我喊道，"这就是那个大红叉！"

我们走进糖果店，店里的招牌上写着：
世界上最棒的糖果店！我信！我从来没在一
个地方看到过那么多糖果。我想把每样都买
来尝尝，可我只有五毛钱。

"利奥,你想吃哪种?"我问。

他说:"这样的来一颗。"

"请给我拿两颗大大的熊软糖。"我对站在柜台后面的人说。

"谢谢你,杰克哥哥!"利奥说道。

"杰克和利奥啊,"那个人问道,"你们就是伯德家的杰克和利奥吗?"

"是我们!"我们告诉他。

那个人伸手从柜台底下拿出一把钥匙。

"有人留下这样东西,让我交给你们。"他说。

　　这把钥匙好大呀，金光闪闪的。这是做什么用的
呢？我看着信封，上面写着：

不要偷看！

回到家再拆开。拿好钥匙，
它会派上用场的！

　　我俩飞快地跑过白桦街，向右一转，到了海鸥大道。我们已经对这个镇上的路开始熟悉了。

　　我们一到家马上拆开信封。里面写着：看看后院树下大石头的旁边吧。

我们发现地上正好有扇小门，我拉开门，有几级向下的台阶。

"来，"我对利奥说，"我先下，你跟着我。"

我兴奋极了，差点儿在台阶上摔跟头。台阶下面，又有一扇门。我把钥匙塞进锁眼。"这就是宝藏！"我说着，深深吸了一口气，推开了门。

我们进到一间秘密的石头小屋！我打开了灯。
"天哪！"利奥感叹道。

"真是太神奇了!"我说完,正好看到墙上的一条横幅。

祝贺你们！小·杰和利奥！

你们成功了！现在，
这间秘密小·屋属于你俩了！

　　我太高兴了，不由自主地跳了起来。利奥也一样，
转着圈地蹦起来。

　　"这是世界上最棒的宝藏啦！"我大声欢呼。

第二天，我们给外公寄去了一张明信片。

明 信 片

亲爱的外公，您送给我们的神秘宝藏，我们好喜欢好喜欢！谢谢您！

To

先生亲
1250号

爱您的杰克和利奥

防晒霜

坐标图

坐标图可以帮助我们确认一个地点的具体位置。

请你帮杰克看一看,怎样从他家到嘉年华游乐场去?

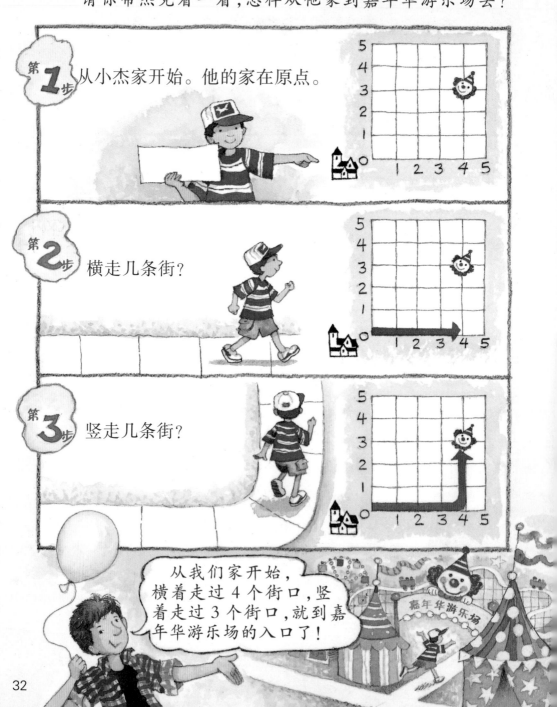

第**1**步 从小杰家开始。他的家在原点。

第**2**步 横走几条街?

第**3**步 竖走几条街?

从我们家开始,横着走过 4 个街口,竖着走过 3 个街口,就到嘉年华游乐场的入口了!

嘉年华游乐场

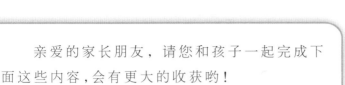

亲爱的家长朋友，请您和孩子一起完成下面这些内容，会有更大的收获哟！

提高阅读能力

• 阅读封面，包括书名等内容。请孩子猜猜，这会是一个什么故事呢？那个男孩手中的图，有什么特别之处？（可能的答案是：图上有一个大大的×，还有很多条格线）。那个孩子胳膊夹着的文件夹上写着什么字？

• 读过故事，请孩子假装自己是那个外公，说说他在搬家到佛罗里达之前，为即将搬来的外孙做了些什么？他在收到两个外孙寄给他的明信片后，会怎么想？

• 在第 19 页，利奥说："我打赌，肯定没有宝藏。"他的猜想对还是不对？

• 书中的两个孩子，对于搬到新家的想法，随着故事情节的发展一点点改变。你说这是为什么呢？

巩固数学概念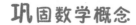

- 请利用第 32 页上的内容，帮孩子学习如何利用坐标图来确定方位。看看孩子是否真正理解杰克说的话，请他找找游泳池的位置。

- 在第 11 页，杰克明白了，坐标图上的横线和竖线，分别代表一条条街道。请孩子假想自己是杰克，他是怎么发现这个奥秘的？（提示：杰克家在拐角处，街角处的街牌也是交叉的，就如同地图上各条街道的交汇处。）

- 请孩子看第 8 页外公的话，理解"先……""再……"的关系。为什么这样做很重要？如果小哥俩儿没有从原点开始，会发生什么情况？请你在每张图中，找到原点的位置。

- 在故事中，一共出现了三张藏宝图，每张图都展示了小杰新家所在小镇的一部分。请孩子将三张地图合成一张完整的小镇地图，用这张图来描述杰克新搬来的这座小镇。

生活中的数学

　　与孩子一起玩寻宝的游戏。在纸上用格线画出住所周边的街道，用✕标出藏宝的位置。请孩子说出，在哪里转弯，走几个街口，才能抵达藏宝的位置。你们可以走路或者开车，但是你们所选的街道都要是比较直的路，这样才可以画出和本书里面一样的坐标图。

　　给孩子一张网格绘图纸，让他画一座藏宝的小岛，在岛上画出树木、岩石或者池塘等。请孩子在小岛上用✕标出藏宝的位置。✕的位置应在横竖两条线的交叉处。最后，家长可以引导孩子用这张小岛藏宝图来编一个海盗藏宝的故事。

请根据提示，找到真正的金蛋。

1.从 0 点出发，先向右走 2 格，再向上走 4 格，是一个真正的金蛋。

2.从 0 点出发，先向上走 4 格，再向右走 6 格，也是一个真正的金蛋。

找不同

从 0 点出发，向右直行，走到第（　）条街，再向上走到第（　）条街，这所房子与其他房子不一样。

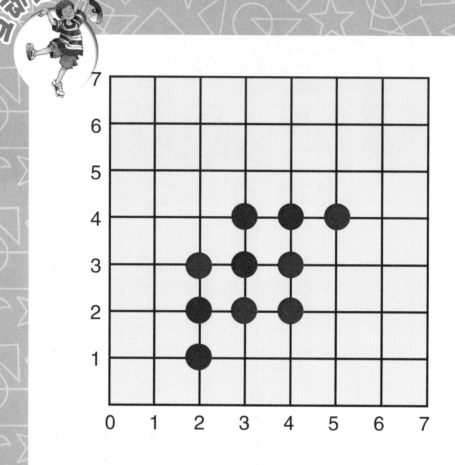

杰克和利奥在玩五子棋。杰克执蓝色棋子，利奥执红色棋子。如果下一步该杰克走的话，他把棋子下在哪个点上，就能获胜了呢?

（1）<!-- 奶牛 -->往左走（ ）格，再往下走（ ）格，可以找到 <!-- 草 -->。

（2）<!-- 兔子 -->往（ ）走（ ）格，再往（ ）走（ ）格，可以找到 <!-- 胡萝卜 -->；或者往（ ）走（ ）格，再往（ ）走（ ）格，也可以找到 <!-- 胡萝卜 -->。

如果苹果用（1,2）表示,那么草莓、葡萄应该怎样表示?开动脑筋想一想。

草莓(,) 葡萄(,)

你能辨认出图中的 10 对双胞胎吗?

(1)(3 , 2)和(2 , 3)

(2)(,)和(,)

(3)(,)和(,)

(4)(,)和(,)

(5)(,)和(,)

(6)(,)和(,)

(7)(,)和(,)

(8)(,)和(,)

(9)(,)和(,)

(10)(,)和(,)

互动练习1：

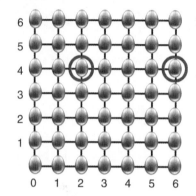

互动练习2：

4,3

互动练习3：

答案不唯一，只要能够描述准确即可。

互动练习4：

(1,1)或(5,5)

互动练习5：

(1)5,1

(2)上,3,左,1,左,1,上,3

互动练习6：

草莓(3,1)

葡萄(3,3)

互动练习7：

(5,1)和(3,4)

(3,3)和(4,4)

(1,1)和(1,4)

(2,1)和(4,1)

(4,3)和(5,3)

(1,2)和(5,2)

(4,2)和(2,4)

(3,1)和(5,4)

(1,3)和(2,2)

(习题设计:董惠平、王　康)

X Marks the Spot!

Why do people have to move? We just did and I don't like it one bit. Neither does my little brother, Leo. But Mom thinks it's great.

"Why did we have to move to a boring old house in a boring old town? " I complain.

"Now, Jake,"Mom says, "this house belonged to Grandpa. He lived here his whole life until he moved to Florida. Isn't that exciting?"

"I guess so,"I say—but I'm just being nice.

Leo and I go outside. A bunch of seagulls dive right over our heads. "Wow!"Leo says. He gets excited about every little thing.

The mail comes. We get a postcard from Grandpa. I read it out loud.

Hi, Jake and Leo! I hope you like the house. It's full of surprises. Check out the attic. Love, Grandpa

We run up to the attic and look around. It's full of old junk. A stuffed owl. Some wooden trunks. A statue of some guy. I'm getting bored.

Then I see a shiny orange folder on the window sill. It says TREASURE MAPS.

"Treasure! " I say. I grab the folder. A letter falls out.

"Listen, Jake,"says Leo."READ BEFORE YOU SEARCH!"

I open the folder. There are three maps and some directions:

· Start at zero.

· First go across.

· Then go up.

· Watch for clues.

"A treasure hunt! " shouts Leo.

"Let's get started! "I tell him.

We look at the first map.

"How do we read this? "Leo asks. He turns the map upside down. He turns it around.

"See the left-hand corner at the bottom? "I say. "That's a picture of this house. We start here. I bet that big ✕ marks the treasure."

We go outside. I stare at the first map again.

"What do we do now, Jake? "asks Leo.

"I'll tell you in a minute,"I say. "Hold your horses."

Actually, this map is not so easy to figure out after all.

Suddenly I get it. "All the lines on the map are streets,"I tell Leo. "Our house is at the corner of Elm Street and Seagull Street."

"I see,"Leo says. "Our house is at zero."

We count two lines across, then three lines up, to the ✕ .

"That's five blocks,"I say. "Not far to walk."

Mom comes to the door. I ask her if we can go explore, but I don't tell her about the treasure. I want her to be surprised.

"This looks like a nice town,"I say. Mom gives me a funny look.

"I'm glad you're starting to like it,"she says. "Be home by supper time."

Leo and I walk along Seagull Street. We count each street we come to. One: Willow Street. Two: Maple Street.

"That dog likes me,"Leo says.

"We'll come back later,"I say. "Now we have to walk up Maple Street."

We turn the corner onto Maple. First we cross Swan Street, then Hawk Street.

"There's a wishing well on Parrot Street," I say. "That must be ✕ !"

"This is nice, but it isn't a treasure," says Leo.

"No, it isn't," I say, "but we can wish we find the treasure."

We close our eyes. I wish hard.

"What if there is no treasure?" Leo asks. "Grandpa's always joking around."

"Not about this," I tell him.

We look at Map 2. This time the wishing well is at zero. So we start there. We walk three blocks along Parrot Street.

Some boys are shooting baskets. They wave to us. I might like it here after all.

We turn up Oak Street — two blocks to go. Leo is walking slowly. "It might be diamonds," I tell him. He walk faster.

After we cross Peacock Street, we come to Owl Street. We both look up. And up. There's an oak tree on the corner. It's the biggest tree I ever saw. The branches on the top are black.

"That tree is creepy," Leo whispers. "Let's go home."

"Are you kidding?" I yell. "We can't go home without the treasure."

"I bet there is no treasure," Leo says. But he looks at the third map with me.

This time the oak tree is at zero. I put my hand over the map. "Don't look," I say to Leo. "I'll give you a clue. Four, one."

"Four, one," Leo says. "That's easy. We go four streets scross and one street up."

"Yes!" I say.

We walk along Owl Street for four blocks. Then we walk up one to Birch Street. There's a candy store on the corner.

"Sweets!" I yell. "This is ✕!"

We go into the store. A sign inside says THE GREATEST CANDY STORE EVER! I believe it. I never saw so much candy in one place. I'd like to buy one of everything, but I just have fifty cents.

"What do you want, Leo?" I ask.

"One of those," he says.

"Two giant gummy bears, please,"I say to the man behind the counter.

"Thanks, Jake! "says Leo.

"Jake and Leo,"the man says."Could you be Jake and Leo Byrd?"

"Yes,"we tell him.

The man reaches under the counter and brings out a key.

"Someone left this for you,"he says.

The key is big. It shines like gold. What is it for? I look at the envelope. It says: *No peeking! Don't open until you get home. Hold onto the key. You'll need it!*

We hurry down Birch Street and turn right on Seagull Street. We're starting to know our way around this town.

The minute we're home I tear open the envelope. Inside it says: *Look in the backyard behind the rock under the tree.*

We find a little door right in the ground! I pull it open. There are steps going down.

"Come on,"I say to Leo."I'll go first."

I am so excited I almost fall down the steps. There is another door at the bottom. I fit the key in the lock."This is it,"I say. I take a deep breath and open the door.

We're in a little stone room. A hidden room. I flip on a light switch.

"Wow!"says Leo.

"This is amazing!"I say. And then I see the sign.

I'm so happy, I start to jump up and down. I can't help it. Leo is jumping around, too.

"This is the best treasure in the whole world!"I shout.

The next day we send a postcard to Grandpa.

Dear Grandpa, we love the "You-know-what".

THANK YOU! ✕✕✕ *Jake and Leo.*